Open Court Reading

Reading and Writing Workbook

Program Authors

Marilyn Jager Adams
Carl Bereiter
Anne McKeough
Robbie Case
Marsha Roit
Jan Hirshberg
Iva Carruthers
Gerald H. Treadway, Jr.

SRA

A Division of The McGraw·Hill Companies

Columbus, Ohio

SRA/McGraw-Hill

*A Division of The **McGraw·Hill** Companies*

Copyright © 2000 by SRA/McGraw-Hill.

All rights reserved. Except as permitted under the United States
Copyright Act, no part of this publication may be reproduced or
distributed in any form or by any means, or stored in a database
or retrieval system, without the prior written permission of the
publisher, unless otherwise indicated.

Send all inquiries to:
SRA/McGraw-Hill
8787 Orion Place
Columbus, OH 43240-4027

Printed in the United States of America.

ISBN 0-02-831063-2

19 20 21 22 23 24 DBH 10 09 08 07

Table *of* Contents

Unit 1

Unit 2

Unit 3

Unit 4

Unit 5

Directions: Find and circle capital letters A, B, C, D, E, F, and G.

Name Lili aga2-1-2010

Letter Recognition • **Reading and Writing Workbook**

Directions: Write small letters *a–h* under the matching capital letters.

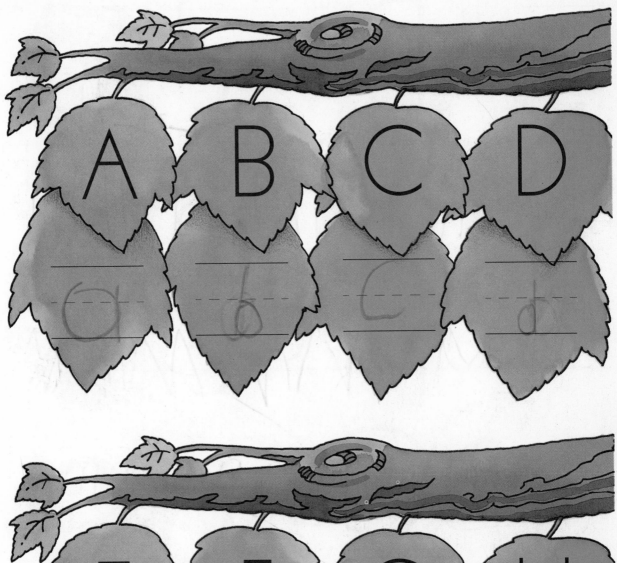

Name Liliana ← ↑ 2010

Directions: Draw a line from the capital letter to its matching small letter.

B   d

D   b

H   c

C   i

I   h

F   f

4   *Letter Recognition* • **Reading and Writing Workbook**

Name _Liliana 2-1-2010_

Directions: Circle the small letter that matches the capital letter.

A   c   e   (a)

E   (e) h l

I   j (i) l

O   c (o) e

U   v w (u)

Name Liliana 2-1-20..

Directions: Practice writing the capital and small forms of the letters Ll, Mm, and Nn.

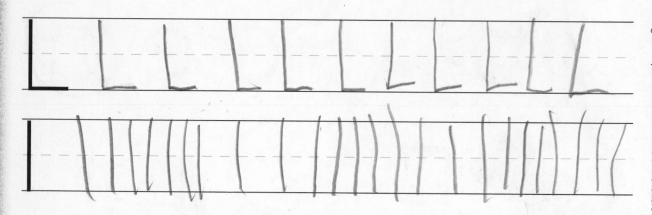

Letter Formation • **Reading and Writing Workbook**

Directions: Connect the dots, in order from A to N, to complete the picture of the bluebird.

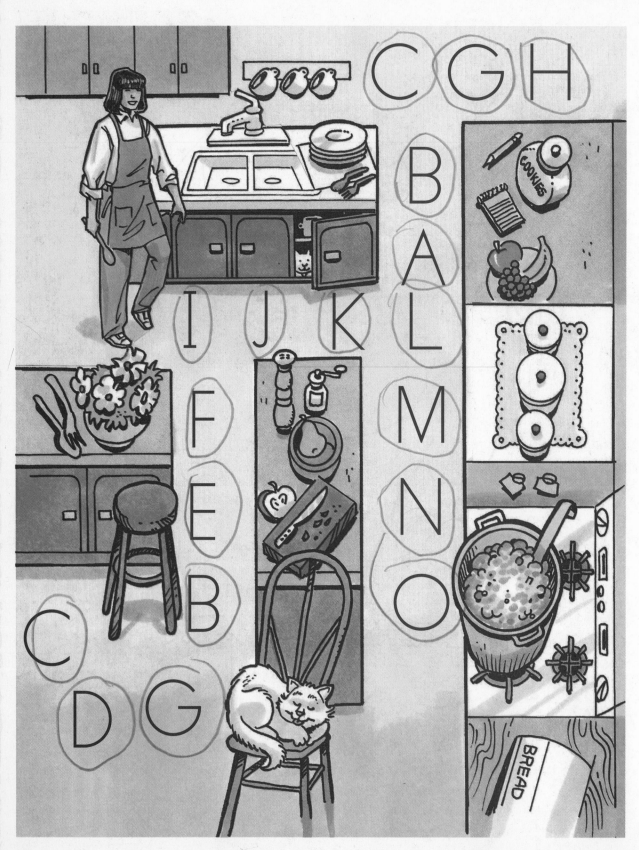

Directions: Connect the capital letters from I to O to help the chef reach the pot at the end of the maze.

Exploring Sounds and Letters • **Reading and Writing Workbook**

Name _____

Directions: Circle each capital letter and draw a line to its matching small letter.

h f s m p j d

Reading and Writing Workbook • *Exploring Sounds and Letters*

9

Ss Ss Ss Ss Ss Ss Ss Ss

Tt Tt Tt Tt Tt Tt Tt Tt

Directions: Write the capital and small forms of the letters Ss and Tt and color the flower petals that match the letter in the center of each flower.

e s
s **S** s
    j p

B   L
t E
R   T
    T

Directions: Write the capital and small forms of the letters *Uu* and *Vv* and color the flower petals that match the letter in the center of each flower.

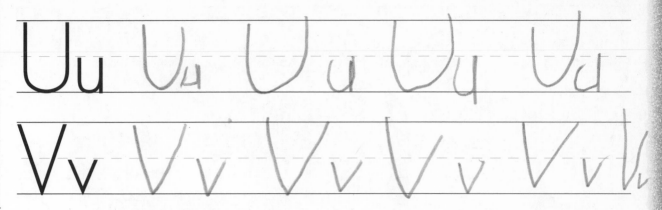

U u   U u   U u   U u   U u   U u

V v   V v   V v   V v   V v   V v   V v

Directions: Circle each capital letter and draw a line to its small form.

Exploring Sounds and Letters • **Reading and Writing Workbook**

Directions: Circle each capital letter and draw a line to its small form.

Name Liliana

Directions: Connect the dots, in order from A to M, to complete the picture of the elm tree.

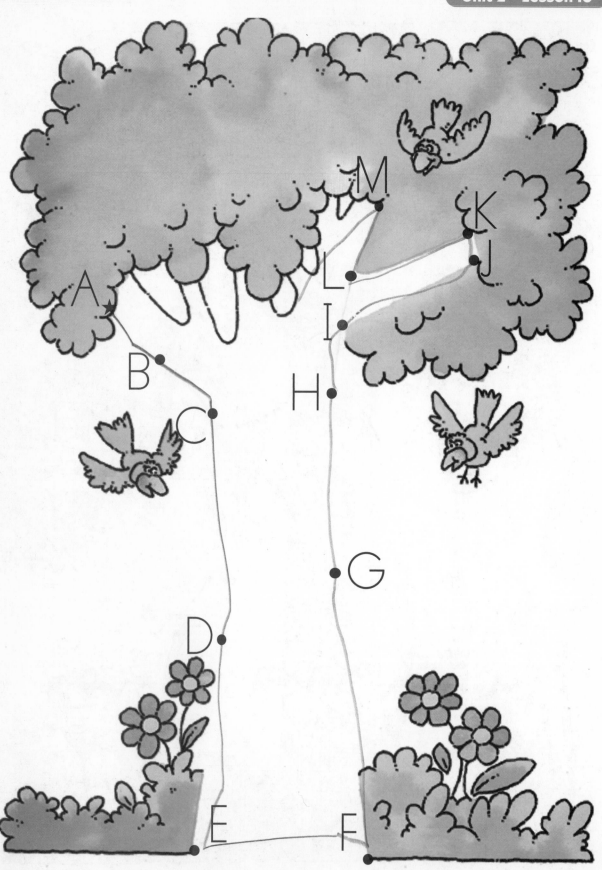

14   *Exploring Sounds and Letters* • **Reading and Writing Workbook**

Name _Lilisa_

Directions: Connect the dots, in order from N to Z, to complete the picture of the willow tree.

Reading and Writing Workbook • *Exploring Sounds and Letters*

Name Lilian

Directions: Write the capital and small forms of the letter Ss. Write the letter s under the picture whose name begins with the sound of s.

Ss

S SSSSSSSSSSSS

S ssssssssssssss

S

p

Exploring Sounds and Letters • **Reading and Writing Workbook**

Directions: Write the letter s under each picture whose name begins with the sound of s.

9

s

2

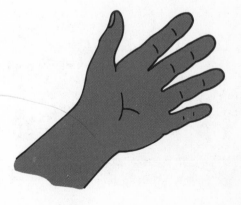

H

S s

Directions: Write the capital and small forms of the letter Ss. Write the letter s under the picture whose name ends with the sound of s.

S S S S S S S S S S S

S S S S S S S S S S S S S S S S S

9

S

Exploring Sounds and Letters • **Reading and Writing Workbook**

Directions: Write the letter s under each picture whose name ends with the sound of s.

q

D

B

B

Name _____

Mm

M M M M M M M M M M M M M M M M

m m m m m m m m m m m m m m m

H

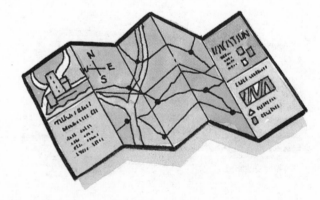

m

Directions: Write the capital and small forms of the letter Mm. Write the letter m under the picture whose name begins with the sound of m.

Exploring Sounds and Letters • **Reading and Writing Workbook**

Directions: Write the letter *m* under each picture whose name begins with the sound of *m*.

F

H

M

K

Name _____

Directions: Write the capital and small forms of the letter *Mm*. Write the letter *m* under the picture whose name ends with the sound of *m*.

Mm

M _____

m _____

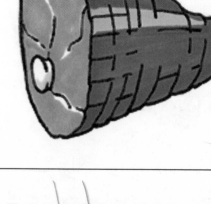

H

H

Exploring Sounds and Letters • **Reading and Writing Workbook**

Directions: Write the letter *m* under each picture whose name ends with the sound of *m*.

D

D

M

D

Name _____

Directions: Write s under each picture whose name begins with the sound of s, and write m under each picture whose name begins with the sound of m.

24

Exploring Sounds and Letters • **Reading and Writing Workbook**

Directions: Write *s* under each picture whose name begins with the sound of *s*, and write *m* under each picture whose name begins with the sound of *m*.

M

S

S

M

Name _Savannah_

Dd

D D D D D D D D D

d d d d d d d d d d

D D D D

M M M

26   *Exploring Sounds and Letters* • **Reading and Writing Workbook**

Name

Directions: Write the letter *d* under each picture whose name begins with the sound of *d*.

P D

B B D

D D D

D D D

Name _____

Dd

Directions: Write the capital and small forms of the letter *Dd*. Write the letter *d* under the picture whose name ends with the sound of *d*.

D _____

d _____

_____

_____

Exploring Sounds and Letters • **Reading and Writing Workbook**

Directions: Write the letter *d* under each picture whose name ends with the sound of *d*.

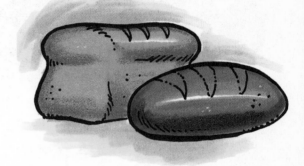

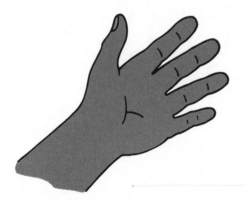

Directions: Write *m, d,* or *s* next to each picture whose name ends with the sound of *m, d,* or *s* to complete the word.

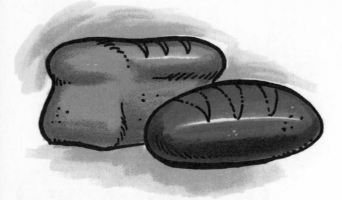

brea

dru

bu

Exploring Sounds and Letters • **Reading and Writing Workbook**

Directions: Write *m*, *d*, or *s* next to each picture whose name ends with the sound of *m*, *d*, or *s* to complete the word.

ha _____

ga _____

be _____

Name _____

P p

P

p

Directions: Write the capital and small forms of the letter *Pp*. Write the letter *p* under the picture whose name begins with the sound of *p*.

32

Exploring Sounds and Letters • **Reading and Writing Workbook**

Directions: Write the letter p under each picture whose name begins with the sound of p.

Name _____

_____

- - - - - - - - - - - - - - - - - - - -

_____

_____

- - - - - - - - - - - - - - - - - - - -

_____

_____

- - - - - - - - - - - - - - - - - - - -

_____

Matching Sounds and Letters • **Reading and Writing Workbook**

Directions: Write the letter *p* under each picture whose name ends with the sound of *p*, and write *m* under each picture whose name ends with the sound of *m*.

Name _____

A

a

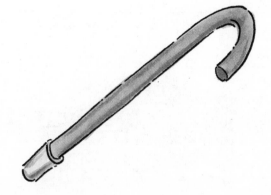

Matching Sounds and Letters • **Reading and Writing Workbook**

Directions: Write the letter a under each picture whose name has the sound of short a in it.

Directions: Circle the word with the sound of short a that names the picture.

bat   cat

hat   pat

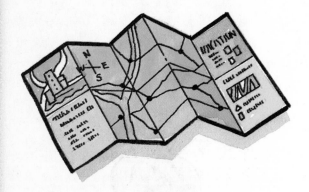

sap   map

sad   pad

Matching Sounds and Letters • **Reading and Writing Workbook**

Directions: Circle the word with the sound of short a that names the picture.

can   cap

_____

- - - - - - - - - - - - - - -

_____

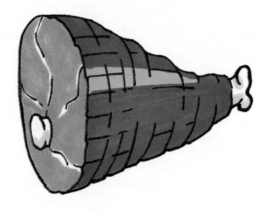

hat   ham

_____

- - - - - - - - - - - - - - -

_____

ram   jam

_____

- - - - - - - - - - - - - - -

_____

man   fan

_____

- - - - - - - - - - - - - - -

_____

Name _____

H _____

h _____

_____

_____

_____

_____

40   *Matching Sounds and Letters* • **Reading and Writing Workbook**

Directions: Write the letter *h* under each picture whose name begins with the sound of *h*.

_____

- - - - - - - - - - - - - -

_____

_____

- - - - - - - - - - - - - -

_____

_____

- - - - - - - - - - - - - -

_____

_____

- - - - - - - - - - - - - -

_____

Directions: Write the capital and small forms of the letter *Tt*. Write the letter *t* under the picture whose name begins with the sound of *t*.

T t

T

t

_____

- - - - - - - - - - - -

_____

_____

- - - - - - - - - - - -

_____

Directions: Write the letter *t* under each picture whose name begins with the sound of *t*.

_____

_ _ _ _ _ _ _ _ _ _ _ _ _ _

_____

_____

_ _ _ _ _ _ _ _ _ _ _ _ _ _

_____

_____

_ _ _ _ _ _ _ _ _ _ _ _ _ _

_____

_____

_ _ _ _ _ _ _ _ _ _ _ _ _ _

_____

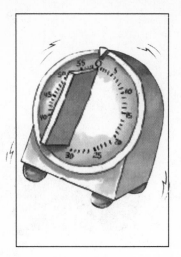

T t

T

t

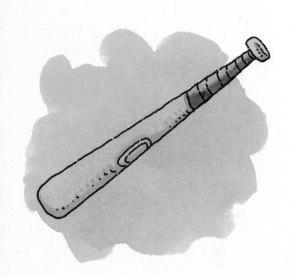

_____   _____

Directions: Write the capital and small forms of the letter Tt. Write the letter t under the picture whose name ends with the sound of t.

Matching Sounds and Letters • **Reading and Writing Workbook**

Directions: Write the letter *t* under each picture whose name ends with the sound of *t*.

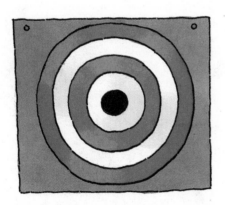

Name _____

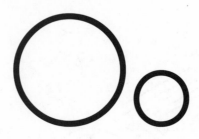

Directions: Write the capital and small forms of the letter Oo. Write the letter o under the picture whose name has the sound of short o.

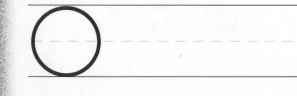

Matching Sounds and Letters • **Reading and Writing Workbook**

Directions: Write the letter o under each picture whose name has the sound of short o.

Name _____

lock   rock

_____

- - - - - - - - - - - - - - - - - - -

_____

mop   tot

_____

- - - - - - - - - - - - - - - - - - -

_____

hot   dog

_____

- - - - - - - - - - - - - - - - - - -

_____

pot   drop

_____

- - - - - - - - - - - - - - - - - - -

_____

Matching Sounds and Letters • **Reading and Writing Workbook**

Directions: Write the letter o under each picture whose name has the sound of short o.

Nn

N _____

n _____

_____   _____

Directions: Write the letter *n* under each picture whose name begins with the sound of *n*.

_____

- - - - - - - - - - - - - - - - -

_____

_____

- - - - - - - - - - - - - - - - -

_____

_____

- - - - - - - - - - - - - - - - -

_____

_____

- - - - - - - - - - - - - - - - -

_____

Name _____

_____

_ _ _ _ _ _ _ _ _ _ _ _ _ _

_____

_____

_ _ _ _ _ _ _ _ _ _ _ _ _ _

_____

_ _ _ _ _ _ _ _ _ _ _ _ _ _

_____

52

Matching Sounds and Letters • **Reading and Writing Workbook**

Name _____

Directions: Write the letter *n* under each picture whose name ends with the sound of *n*.

Directions: Write the capital and small forms of the letter Aa. Write the letter a under the picture whose name has the sound of short a.

Aa

A

a

Name _____

Directions: Write the letter a under each picture whose name has the sound of short a.

_____

- - - - - - - - - - - - - -

_____

_____

- - - - - - - - - - - - - -

_____

_____

- - - - - - - - - - - - - -

_____

_____

- - - - - - - - - - - - - -

_____

Reading and Writing Workbook • *Matching Sounds and Letters*   **55**

A

a

_____

_____

Matching Sounds and Letters • **Reading and Writing Workbook**

Directions: Write the letter a under each picture whose name has the sound of long a.

_____

- - - - - - - - - - - - - - -

_____

_____

- - - - - - - - - - - - - - -

_____

_____

- - - - - - - - - - - - - - -

_____

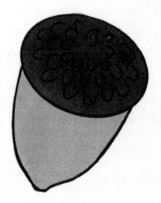

_____

- - - - - - - - - - - - - - -

_____

Name _____

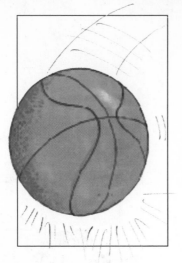

Bb

Directions: Write the capital and small forms of the letter Bb. Write the letter b under the picture whose name begins with the sound of b.

B

b

Matching Sounds and Letters • **Reading and Writing Workbook**

Directions: Write the letter *b* under each picture whose name begins with the sound of *b*.

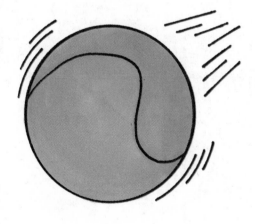

Name _____

Matching Sounds and Letters • **Reading and Writing Workbook**

Name _____

Directions: Circle all the pictures that begin with the sound of *b*.

Directions: Write the capital and small forms of the letter Cc. Write the letter c under the picture whose name begins with the sound of c (/k/).

C c

C

C

Matching Sounds and Letters • **Reading and Writing Workbook**

Directions: Write the letter c under each picture whose name begins with the sound of c (/k/).

Unit 3 • Lesson 16

Directions: Follow the maze and circle each stone with a picture whose name begins with the sound of c (/k/) to help the Prince find his castle.

Matching Sounds and Letters • **Reading and Writing Workbook**

Name _____

Directions: Follow the maze and circle each stone with a picture whose name ends with the sound of c (/k/) to help the Princess find her crown.

Directions: Write the capital and small forms of the letter *Dd*. Write the letter *d* under the picture whose name begins with the sound of *d*.

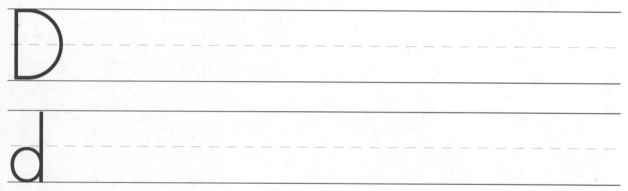

Matching Sounds and Letters • **Reading and Writing Workbook**

Directions: Write the letter *d* under each picture whose name begins with the sound of *d*.

E e

E ---------------------------------

e ---------------------------------

_____   _____

_____   _____

Matching Sounds and Letters • **Reading and Writing Workbook**

Directions: Write the capital and small forms of the letter Ee. Write the letter e under the picture whose name has the sound of short e.

Directions: Write the letter e under each picture whose name has the sound of short e.

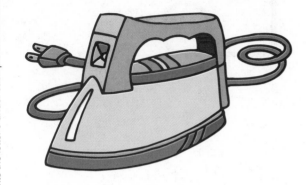

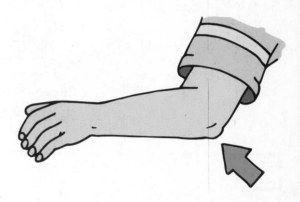

_____

- - - - - - - - - - -

_____

_____

- - - - - - - - - - -

_____

_____

- - - - - - - - - - -

_____

_____

- - - - - - - - - - -

_____

Name _____

E e E e

E

e

_____   _____

- - - - - - - - - - - - - -   - - - - - - - - - - - - - -

_____   _____

Matching Sounds and Letters • **Reading and Writing Workbook**

Directions: Write the letter e under each picture whose name has the sound of long e.

_____

- - - - - - - - - - - - - - -

_____

_____

- - - - - - - - - - - - - - -

_____

_____

- - - - - - - - - - - - - - -

_____

_____

- - - - - - - - - - - - - - -

_____

F f

F _ _ _ _ _ _ _ _ _ _ _ _ _ _ _ _ _ _ _

f _ _ _ _ _ _ _ _ _ _ _ _ _ _ _ _ _ _ _

_____ _____

Directions: Write the letter *f* under each picture whose name begins with the sound of *f*.

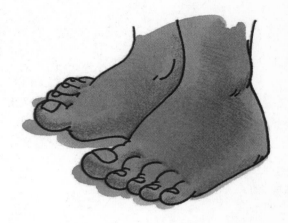

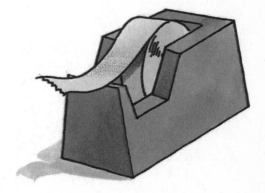

Name _____

Matching Sounds and Letters • **Reading and Writing Workbook**

Name _____

Directions: Circle the objects in the picture whose names end with the sound of *f*.

_____

- - - - - - - - - - - - - - - - - - - -

_____

Reading and Writing Workbook • *Matching Sounds and Letters*

75

Directions: Write the capital and small forms of the letter Gg. Write the letter g under the picture whose name begins with the sound of g.

G g

G

g

Matching Sounds and Letters • **Reading and Writing Workbook**

Name _____

Directions: Write the letter *g* under each picture whose name begins with the sound of *g*.

_____

- - - - - - - - - - - - -

_____

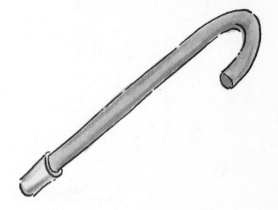

_____

- - - - - - - - - - - - -

_____

_____

- - - - - - - - - - - - -

_____

_____

- - - - - - - - - - - - -

_____

Directions: Circle the word with the final sound of /g/ that names the picture.

pig   wig

_____

- - - - - - - - - - - - - - -

_____

rug   bug

_____

- - - - - - - - - - - - - - -

_____

pig   fig

_____

- - - - - - - - - - - - - - -

_____

ladybug   hug

_____

- - - - - - - - - - - - - - -

_____

Matching Sounds and Letters • **Reading and Writing Workbook**

Directions: Circle the word with the final sound of /g/ that names the picture.

log   hog

_____

- - - - - - - - - - - -

_____

egg   leg

_____

- - - - - - - - - - - -

_____

hog   dog

_____

- - - - - - - - - - - -

_____

bug   mug

_____

- - - - - - - - - - - -

_____

Name _____

Hh

Directions: Write the capital and small forms of the letter *Hh*. Write the letter *h* under the picture whose name begins with the sound of *h*.

H _____

h _____

_____   _____

Matching Sounds and Letters • **Reading and Writing Workbook**

Directions: Write the letter *h* under each picture whose name begins with the sound of *h*.

_____

_____

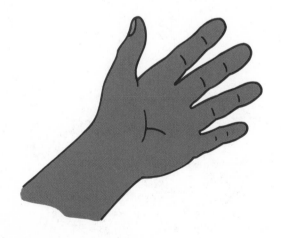

_____

_____

Directions: Write the capital and small forms of the letter *Ii*. Write the letter *i* under the picture whose name has the sound of short *i*.

I i

I

i

_____   _____
- - - - - - - - - - -   - - - - - - - - - - -
_____   _____

Directions: Write the letter *i* under each picture whose name has the sound of short *i*.

Name _____

Directions: Write the capital and small forms of the letter *Ii*. Write the letter *i* under the picture whose name has the sound of long *i*.

I i   I i

I _____

i _____

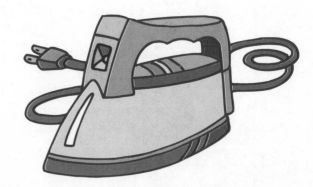

_____   _____

_____   _____

Matching Sounds and Letters • **Reading and Writing Workbook**

Directions: Write the letter *i* under each picture whose name has the sound of long *i*.

Name _____

Directions: Write the capital and small forms of the letter *Jj*. Write the letter *j* under the picture whose name begins with the sound of *j*.

J

j

_____   _____

_____   _____

Directions: Write the letter *j* under each picture whose name begins with the sound of *j*.

Name _____

Directions: Write the capital and small forms of the letter Kk. Write the letter k under the picture whose name begins with the sound of k.

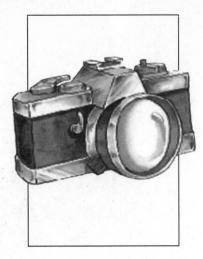

Kk

K

k

88   *Matching Sounds and Letters* • **Reading and Writing Workbook**

Directions: Write the letter k under each picture whose name begins with the sound of k.

_____

- - - - - - - - - - - - - - -

_____

_____

- - - - - - - - - - - - - - -

_____

_____

- - - - - - - - - - - - - - -

_____

_____

- - - - - - - - - - - - - - -

_____

L l

Directions: Write the capital and small forms of the letter *Ll*. Write the letter *l* under the picture whose name begins with the sound of *l*.

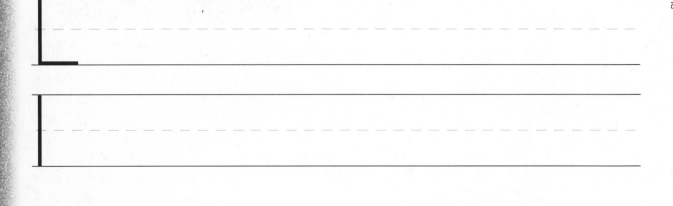

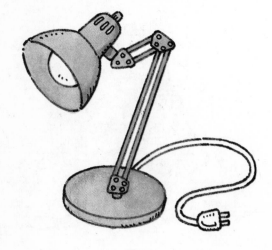

Matching Sounds and Letters • **Reading and Writing Workbook**

Directions: Write the letter *l* under each picture whose name begins with the sound of *l*.

Name _____

Matching Sounds and Letters • Reading and Writing Workbook

Directions: Find and circle all the objects in the picture that end with the sound of *l*.

Directions: Write the capital and small forms of the letter *Mm*. Write the letter *m* under the picture whose name ends with the sound of *m*.

Mm

M

m

Matching Sounds and Letters • **Reading and Writing Workbook**

Directions: Write the letter *m* under each picture whose name ends with the sound of *m*.

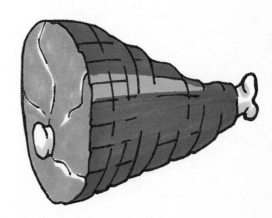

Name _____

Nn

N

n

Directions: Write the capital and small forms of the letter Nn. Write the letter n under the picture whose name begins with the sound of n.

Matching Sounds and Letters • **Reading and Writing Workbook**

Directions: Write the letter *n* under each picture whose name begins with the sound of *n*.

Name _____

_____

_ _ _ _ _ _ _ _ _ _ _ _ _ _ _ _ _ _ _

_____

Matching Sounds and Letters • **Reading and Writing Workbook**

Name _____

Directions: Circle all the items in the cart that end with the sound of *n*.

Name _____

Directions: Write the capital and small forms of the letter Oo. Write the letter o under the picture whose name has the sound of long o in it.

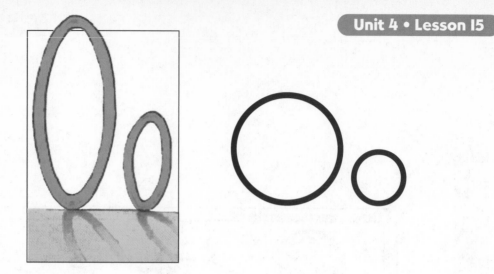

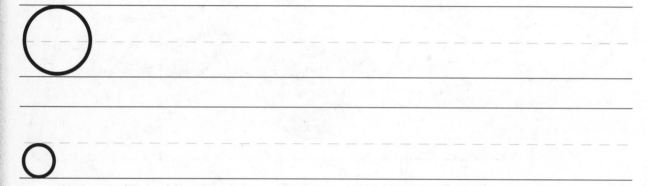

Matching Sounds and Letters • **Reading and Writing Workbook**

Name _____

Directions: Write the letter o under each picture whose name has the sound of long o.

_____
- -
_____

_____
- -
_____

_____
- -
_____

_____
- -
_____

Name _____

P p

P

p

_____

Matching Sounds and Letters • **Reading and Writing Workbook**

Directions: Write the letter *p* under each picture whose name ends with the sound of *p*.

_____

- - - - - - - - - - - - - - - - -

_____

_____

- - - - - - - - - - - - - - - - -

_____

_____

- - - - - - - - - - - - - - - - -

_____

_____

- - - - - - - - - - - - - - - - -

_____

Directions: Write the capital and small forms of the letter Qq. Write the letter q under the picture whose name begins with the sound of q.

Qq

Q _____

q _____

_____   _____

Directions: Write the letter *q* under each picture whose name begins with the sound of *q*.

_____

_ _ _ _ _ _ _ _ _ _ _ _ _

_____

_____

_ _ _ _ _ _ _ _ _ _ _ _ _

_____

_____

_ _ _ _ _ _ _ _ _ _ _ _ _

_____

_____

_ _ _ _ _ _ _ _ _ _ _ _ _

_____

Name _____

Directions: Write the capital and small forms of the letter *Rr*. Write the letter *r* under the picture whose name begins with the sound of *r*.

R r

R _____

r _____

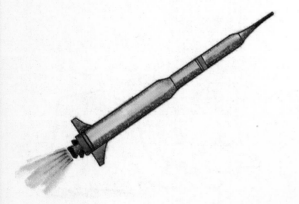

_____

_____

Directions: Write the letter r under each picture whose name begins with the sound of r.

_____

_ _ _ _ _ _ _ _ _ _ _ _

_____

_____

_ _ _ _ _ _ _ _ _ _ _ _

_____

_____

_ _ _ _ _ _ _ _ _ _ _ _

_____

_____

_ _ _ _ _ _ _ _ _ _ _ _

_____

Directions: Write the letter r under each picture whose name ends with the sound of r.

_____

- - - - - - - - - - - - - - -

_____

_____

- - - - - - - - - - - - - - -

_____

_____

- - - - - - - - - - - - - - -

_____

Directions: Write the letter r under each picture whose name ends with the sound of r.

Name _____

S s

Directions: Write the capital and small forms of the letter Ss. Write the letter s under the picture whose name begins with the sound of s.

S _____

s _____

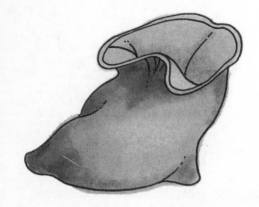

_____   _____

110   *Matching Sounds and Letters* • **Reading and Writing Workbook**

Name

Directions: Write the letter s under each picture whose name begins with the sound of s.

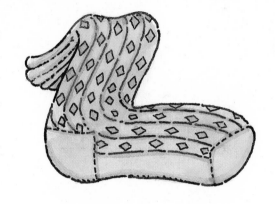

Directions: Write the capital and small forms of the letter Tt. Write a capital T under the picture whose name begins with the sound of t.

T t

T

t

Matching Sounds and Letters • **Reading and Writing Workbook**

Directions: Write a capital *T* under each picture whose name begins with the sound of *t* and write a small *t* under the picture that ends with the sound of *t*.

Directions: Write the capital and small forms of the letter *Uu*. Write the letter *u* under the picture whose name has the sound of short *u* in it.

Uu

U

u

Matching Sounds and Letters • **Reading and Writing Workbook**

Directions: Write the letter *u* under each picture whose name has the sound of short *u* in it.

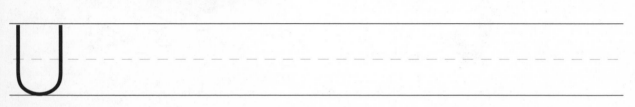

Directions: Write the capital and small forms of the letter *Uu*. Write the letter *u* under the picture whose name has the sound of long *u*.

U

u

Directions: Write the letter *u* under each picture whose name has the sound of long *u*.

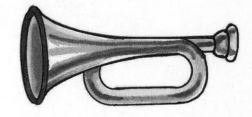

Name _____

Directions: Write the capital and small forms of the letter Vv. Write the letter v under the picture whose name begins with the sound of v.

V

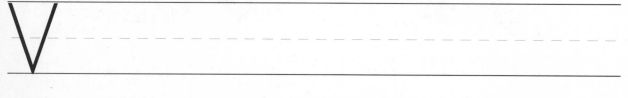

V

v

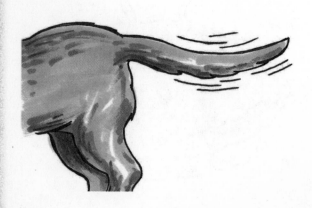

_____

_____

118

Matching Sounds and Letters • **Reading and Writing Workbook**

Directions: Write the letter *v* under each picture whose name begins with the sound of *v*.

_____

- - - - - - - - - - - -

_____

_____

- - - - - - - - - - - -

_____

_____

- - - - - - - - - - - -

_____

_____

- - - - - - - - - - - -

_____

Name _____

W w

W

w

Matching Sounds and Letters • **Reading and Writing Workbook**

Directions: Write the letter w under each picture whose name begins with the sound of w.

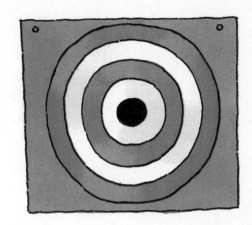

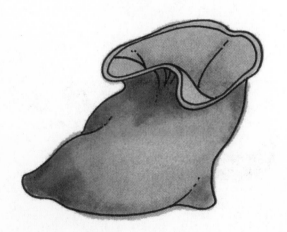

Directions: Write the capital and small forms of the letter Xx. Write the letter x under the picture whose name ends with the sound of x.

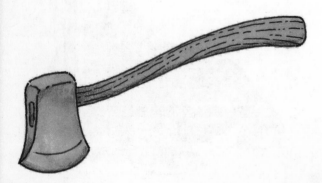

Matching Sounds and Letters • **Reading and Writing Workbook**

Name _____

Directions: Write the letter x under each picture whose name ends with the sound of x.

_____

_____

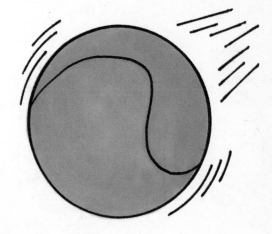

_____

_____

Name _____

Directions: Write the capital and small forms of the letter Yy. Write the letter y under the picture whose name begins with the sound of y.

Y _____

y _____

_____   _____

124   *Matching Sounds and Letters* • **Reading and Writing Workbook**

Directions: Write the letter y under each picture whose name begins with the sound of y.

_____

_____

_____

_____

_____

_____

_____

_____

Directions: Write the capital and small forms of the letter Zz. Write the letter z under the picture whose name begins with the sound of z.

Z z

Z

z

Matching Sounds and Letters • **Reading and Writing Workbook**

Directions: Write the letter z under each picture whose name begins with the sound of z.

Name _____

Writing Letters • **Reading and Writing Workbook**

Directions: Choose your own letters to write.

Directions: Choose your own letters to write.

383-AAC-523

383-AAC-523